"A thousand generations live in you now. But this is your fight."
- LUKE SKYWALKER

STAR WARS™

ANNUAL 2020

EGMONT

We bring stories to life

First published in Great Britain 2019 by Egmont UK Limited
The Yellow Building, 1 Nicholas Road, London W11 4AN

Written by Ned Hartley
Designed by Richie Hull and Maddox Philpot
Cover design by Richie Hull

© & ™ 2019 Lucasfilm Ltd.
ISBN 978 1 4052 9449 2
70381/001
Printed in Italy

To find more great *Star Wars* books, visit www.egmont.co.uk/starwars

CHOOSE YOUR DESTINY

Pick your team and join the fight!

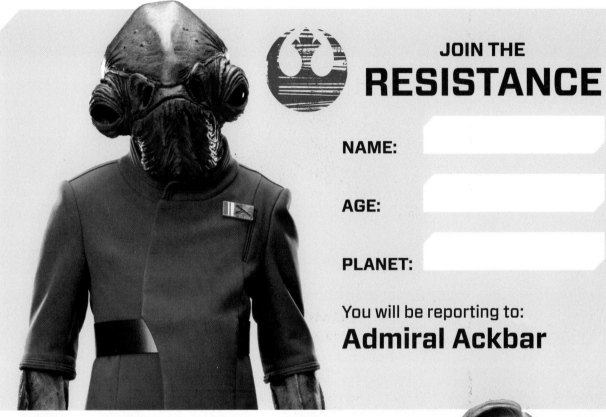

JOIN THE
RESISTANCE

NAME:

AGE:

PLANET:

You will be reporting to:
Admiral Ackbar

JOIN THE
FIRST ORDER

NAME:

AGE:

PLANET:

You will be reporting to:
General Hux

WHO'S WHO!

The fate of the galaxy was changed by just a few people! Find out the real story behind these incredible heroes and villains.

Anakin Skywalker

One of the most powerful Jedi who ever lived, Anakin Skywalker grew up on the remote desert planet of Tatooine. Anakin was trained by Obi-Wan Kenobi, and the two fought side by side for years during the Clone Wars. Anakin was turned to the dark side of the Force by Chancellor Palpatine, and ended up fighting his former master Obi-Wan. Anakin was badly hurt during this fight, and encased himself in a suit of armour, becoming known as Darth Vader!

Best moment: Anakin's duel with Obi-Wan on the fire planet of Mustafar was one of the most exciting battles ever!

Padmé Amidala

Padmé was the Queen of Naboo and later a senator in the Galactic Senate. She was a brave and clever leader who cared deeply for her people, and was pretty handy in a firefight too. Padmé married Anakin Skywalker, even though their romance was forbidden by the Jedi council – she died shortly after giving birth to twins Luke and Leia.

Best moment: Padmé often disguised herself as a handmaiden so that she was less of a target for assassins. Smart!

Obi-Wan Kenobi

Obi-Wan was a Jedi who thought that he could train Anakin Skywalker and keep him from the dark side of the Force. After he fought Anakin on Mustafar, Obi-Wan hid Anakin and Padmé's children, giving Leia to Senator Organa and taking Luke to Anakin's half-brother Owen on Tatooine. Obi-Wan stayed on Tatooine and finally gave Luke his father's lightsaber when he was ready.

Best moment: Obi-Wan bravely stood up against Darth Vader and was struck down, allowing Luke, Han and Leia to escape the Death Star.

Luke Skywalker

Growing up, Luke never knew the true story of his parents. It wasn't until he fought Darth Vader in Cloud City that he found out that Vader was his father. Luke finally helped his father get some form of redemption when Vader died on the second Death Star. After the Galactic Civil War, Luke tried to set up an academy for new Jedi, but it was destroyed by Kylo Ren.

Best moment: Luke destroyed the first Death Star when he turned off the targeting computer and used the Force to fire a proton torpedo into a tiny vent. Boom!

Leia Organa

A founding member of the Rebel Alliance and fierce military leader, Princess Leia Organa delivered the Death Star plans to Obi-Wan Kenobi and was vital in the destruction of the battle station. Leia fell in love with Han Solo, and the two married and had a child, Kylo Ren. When she saw the First Order growing in power, Leia created the Resistance to fight back.

Best moment: Leia befriended the Ewoks on Endor, convincing them to join the fight and turn the tide against the Empire.

Han Solo

This confident scoundrel grew up on the mean streets of Corellia and became an intergalactic smuggler. Han became involved with the Rebel Alliance, and proved himself to be a hero time and time again, using his ship, the *Millennium Falcon*, to fight the Empire. Life was hard for Han after the Galactic Civil War, and he became estranged from his wife Leia and his son Ben.

Best moment: Han and Luke rescued Princess Leia from the Death Star using skill, intelligence and lots of blaster power!

Chewbacca

This heroic Wookiee first met Han Solo when Chewie was being held as a prisoner by the Empire on the planet Mimban. Han helped him escape and the two were firm friends ever since. Chewie was Han's co-pilot on the *Millennium Falcon*, helping him navigate his way out of every tough scrape. Chewbacca was 190 years old when he first met Han – he looked good for his age!

Best moment: When the rebels were outnumbered on the forest moon of Endor, Chewie stole an Imperial Walker, helping save the day.

Yoda

Yoda was one of the wisest Jedi Masters who ever lived, and he understood more about the Force than almost anyone. When the Galactic Empire took control of the galaxy, Yoda hid on the swamp planet, Dagobah, where Luke Skywalker later found him for training.

Best moment: Yoda was a ferocious fighter. His battle with Palpatine destroyed the Senate chambers with the sheer amount of power involved.

Emperor Palpatine

One of the most evil people who ever lived, Emperor Palpatine was also a Sith known as Darth Sidious. He turned Anakin Skywalker to the dark side of the Force, transforming him into Darth Vader. Palpatine then took over the galaxy, mercilessly ruling the Galactic Empire.

Best moment: Palpatine's scariest moment was when he attacked Luke Skywalker using Force lightning! Terrifying!

Rey

Rey grew up scavenging to survive on the planet Jakku. She was drawn to Luke Skywalker's lightsaber, feeling the pull of the Force. Rey sought out Luke on Ahch-To, but he was reluctant to teach her at first. Rey was incredibly strong in the Force, and drew the attention of Supreme Leader Snoke and Kylo Ren. Although they couldn't turn her to the dark side, Rey struggled to find her place in the galaxy.

Best moment: Rey's climactic battle with Kylo Ren on the disintegrating Starkiller Base was nailbiting stuff!

Finn

A former stormtrooper known as FN-2187, Finn rebelled against his training and helped Poe Dameron escape from the First Order by stealing a TIE fighter. Finn's exciting journey took him to the planet Jakku where he met Rey and BB-8, and then to Starkiller Base, which he helped destroy. Finn still struggled with being a hero, but he would do anything for his new friends.

Best moment: Finn was bravest when he stood up against his former commander Captain Phasma.

Poe Dameron

Poe was the best pilot in the Resistance, but he found it hard to take orders from anyone. Poe flew his special black X-wing with his astromech droid and friend BB-8. Poe said that he could fly anything, which was good because his adventures meant that he ended up in the cockpit of lots of different types of starship!

Best moment: Poe helped lead the surviving Resistance members out of the salt mines on Crait.

Kylo Ren

Born Ben Solo, Kylo Ren was the son of Leia and Han. Kylo Ren trained to be a Jedi in Luke Skywalker's Jedi Academy but Supreme Leader Snoke turned him to the dark side. Kylo Ren joined the First Order, and even killed his own father! He attempted to get Rey to join him, and even kills his master, but ultimately the two were destined to be enemies.

Best moment: Kylo Ren used the Force to stop blaster fire in mid-air when he captured Poe Dameron – he's so powerful!

STAR WARS
THE PHANTOM MENACE

Anakin Skywalker begins his journey, and a great evil starts to reveal itself.

Jedi Qui-Gon Jinn and Obi-Wan Kenobi rescue Queen Padmé Amidala of Naboo from an attack by the Trade Federation, but their ship is damaged and they are forced to land for repairs on the desert planet of Tatooine.

They meet young Anakin Skywalker, who Qui-Gon senses is very strong with the Force. Anakin takes part in an exciting podrace and wins his freedom! Just as they are about to leave Tatooine, Qui-Gon fights Darth Maul, a new and mysterious opponent with a dangerous double-bladed lightsaber.

Padmé returns to Naboo and leads her people against the Trade Federation's droid army, but it looks like the droids have the upper hand. During the massive battle, Anakin hides on a starfighter and manages to blast the control ship, shutting down the droid army! Meanwhile Obi-Wan and Qui-Gon fight Darth Maul, but Qui-Gon is mortally wounded. Obi-Wan finally beats Darth Maul and he promises a dying Qui-Gon Jinn that he will train young Anakin Skywalker to become a Jedi.

PODRACE SHORTCUT!

Anakin is racing a new route in his podracer and he doesn't know the best way to go. Which route should he take to get to the finish?

A   B   C

FINISH

ANSWERS ON PAGE 69

STAR WARS

ATTACK OF THE CLONES

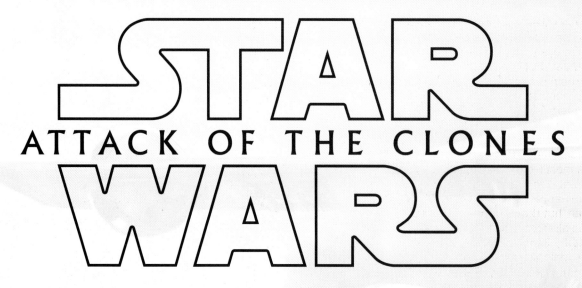

Obi-Wan discovers a sinister galaxy-wide plot, and Anakin and Padmé head down a dangerous path.

The evil Count Dooku leads the Separatist movement against the Galactic Republic, and the galaxy is on the brink of war! Senator Padmé Amidala is nearly assassinated by Zam Wessel, but Wessel is killed by bounty hunter Jango Fett before Obi-Wan can get any information from her. Obi-Wan tracks Jango to the ocean planet Kamino where he finds a secret clone army ready to fight for the Republic.

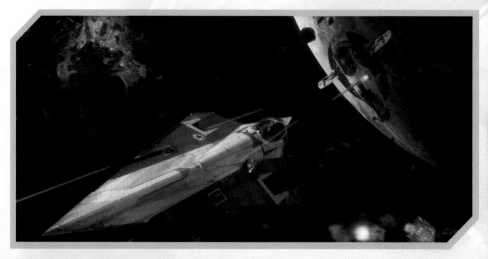

Meanwhile, Jedi Padawan Anakin has been assigned to protect Padmé, and the two soon fall in love. They travel back to Tatooine where Anakin finds his mother has been killed by Tusken Raiders.

Obi-Wan discovers that the Separatists are meeting on Geonosis, but he is captured by Count Dooku's forces. Anakin and Padme come to rescue Obi-Wan, but they are also captured and all three are thrown in the deadly Geonosis arena – where wild animals are about to eat them! The Jedi and the clone army arrive in the nick of time and fight the Separatist droid army, becoming the first battle in the Clone Wars.

THE CLONE WARS

The fight between the Republic clone army and the droid army was known as the Clone Wars. The Jedi fought on the same side as the clones, while Count Dooku and the Sith were in charge of the droid army.

ODD CLONE OUT

There has been a mistake in the cloning process!
Which of these clones is different from the others?

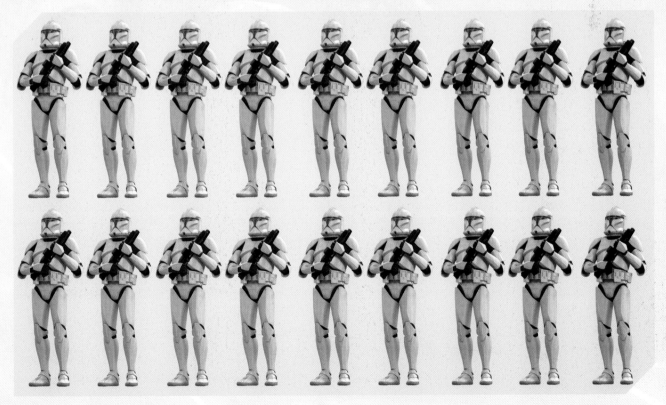

ANSWERS ON PAGE 69

STAR WARS
REVENGE OF THE SITH

Anakin becomes Darth Vader while Palpatine seizes power!

In an exciting space battle over the planet city of Coruscant, Obi-Wan and Anakin rescue Supreme Chancellor Palpatine from General Grievous, not realising that Palpatine had secretly organised the whole thing. On Coruscant Padmé tells Anakin that she is pregnant, and Anakin begins to have visions of her dying. Palpatine starts to convince Anakin to move against the Jedi Council, telling him that the only way to save Padmé is to turn to the dark side of the Force.

Anakin becomes a Sith, assuming the name Darth Vader. He attacks the Jedi Council, and at the same time Palpatine issues Order 66, an order that tells the clone army to kill the Jedi they are fighting alongside. Obi-Wan and Vader battle on the planet Mustafar, and Obi-Wan wins, nearly killing Vader. Obi-Wan tries to help Padmé, but she dies after giving birth to Luke and Leia, so Obi-Wan hides them, hoping that they will grow up to save the galaxy. Palpatine gives Vader a formidable suit of armour, and the rule of the Galactic Empire begins ...

FIGHT THE EMPIRE!

The crew of the *Ghost* were one of the many teams who stood up against the Empire, and were part of the movement that became the Rebel Alliance!

SITH SUDOKU

1 2 3 4 5 6

Complete the grid by making sure there is only one image of each character in each row, column and 2x3 box.

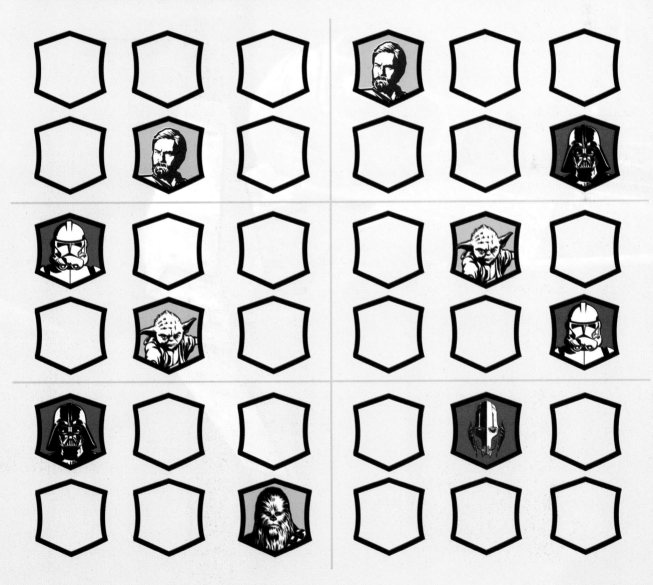

THE BEST SHIPS!

Your round up of the coolest ships that ever graced space!

Naboo starfighter

Affiliation: The Royal House of Naboo
Weapons: Two blaster cannons and a proton torpedo launcher

This sleek and shiny starfighter doesn't just look good, it's also incredibly fast and has enough firepower to take down larger targets. There's only room for one pilot, but an astromech droid fits neatly behind. Naboo Starfighters were used to fight the Trade Federation, and young Anakin Skywalker found himself in the cockpit of one!

Jedi starfighter

Affiliation: The Jedi Order
Weapons: Dual laser cannons

These starfighters were specifically designed for Jedi, and only someone with Force-enhanced reflexes could move fast enough to pilot their special controls. Anakin Skywalker and Obi-Wan Kenobi both flew these supercool ships during the Clone Wars, using their superior speed and agility to evade their enemies.

Slave I

Affiliation: Boba and Jango Fett, the Galactic Empire
Weapons: Blaster cannons, laser cannons, seismic charges, concussion missiles

Originally owned by bounty hunter Jango Fett, *Slave I* was passed down to Jango's son Boba Fett after his death. It's one of the most dangerous ships in the galaxy and is specially modified so it can match the flying pattern of any other ship. Boba used *Slave I* to track the *Millennium Falcon* for Darth Vader, delivering Han Solo to the Sith Lord.

X-wing

Affiliation: Rebel Alliance
Weapons: Laser cannons, proton torpedo launcher

The symbol of the Rebel Alliance, X-wings are fast, strong and powerful - everything you need in a starfighter! Their strong shields mean that they can take lots of damage and their hyperdrives allow them to jump in and out of battle as needed. The name X-wing comes from the X shape that their S-foils make when opened.

TIE fighter

Affiliation: Galactic Empire
Weapons: Laser cannons

These short-range starfighters are seen throughout the Empire. Although they aren't the most powerful ships, a squadron of these can swarm and destroy more powerful starfighters. TIE fighters are not equipped with hyperdrives, so they need a larger Star Destroyer or freighter to bring them to and from battles.

Y-wing

Affiliation: Rebel Alliance
Weapons: Laser cannons, proton torpedo launchers, proton bombs

Y-wings were most commonly used by the Rebel Alliance for bombing raids, dropping powerful proton bombs on their enemies. A squadron of Y-wings can take down a huge Imperial Star Destroyer if they have enough protection from other starfighters.

TIE Advanced

Affiliation: Galactic Empire
Weapons: Laser cannons

Darth Vader flew a very special prototype ship, with a cockpit specially designed for his armour. Vader proved himself as an expert pilot in the Clone Wars, and the fast and agile TIE Advanced only made him even deadlier. It was fitted with a hyperdrive, which allowed him to escape after the destruction of the Death Star.

Special Forces TIE fighter

Affiliation: The First Order
Weapons: Laser cannons

First Order Special Forces use stronger, more powerful TIE fighters than the rest of the First Order - they have a special red stripe on the cockpit to show they are different from other TIE fighters. Their starfighters have space for a pilot and a gunner, who are placed in the cockpit back to back.

Black One

Affiliation: The Resistance
Weapons: Laser cannons, dual weapon pod, blaster cannon

Poe Dameron's personal T-70 X-wing, *Black One* delivered the critical blows against Starkiller Base, returning to D'Qar with a bad case of carbon-scoring and frayed fire-control linkages. The X-wing played a key role in the attack on a First Order Dreadnought, but was destroyed by Kylo Ren's attack run against the *Raddus*.

TIE silencer

Affiliation: The First Order
Weapons: Laser cannons, proton torpedo launchers

Kylo Ren flies one of the most powerful starfighters in the First Order fleet. It has powerful heavy lasers for attacking Resistance cruisers and has a special stealth field generator so that it is invisible on enemy sensors. The TIE silencer is a prototype, and only Kylo Ren gets to fly one.

Resistance bomber

Affiliation: The Resistance
Weapons: Laser cannons, proton bombs

These huge, hulking ships are some of the most powerful ships in the Resistance. They carry hundreds of powerful protons bombs which can destroy much larger ships. Resistance bombers have gun turrets at the back and the bottom of the ship, so that gunners can protect the ship during bombing runs.

Millennium Falcon

Affiliation: The Rebel Alliance, The Resistance
Weapons: Two heavy laser cannons, two quad lasers, two missile tubes, tractor beam

Han Solo originally won the *Millennium Falcon* from gambler Lando Calrissian in a card game of Sabacc. The *Falcon* was an important part of the Rebel Alliance, helping destroy the second Death Star. Han lost the ship after the fall of the Empire, and it was eventually found on Jakku by Rey. The *Falcon* is one of the fastest ships in the galaxy, and the coolest!

DRAW THE
MILLENNIUM FALCON

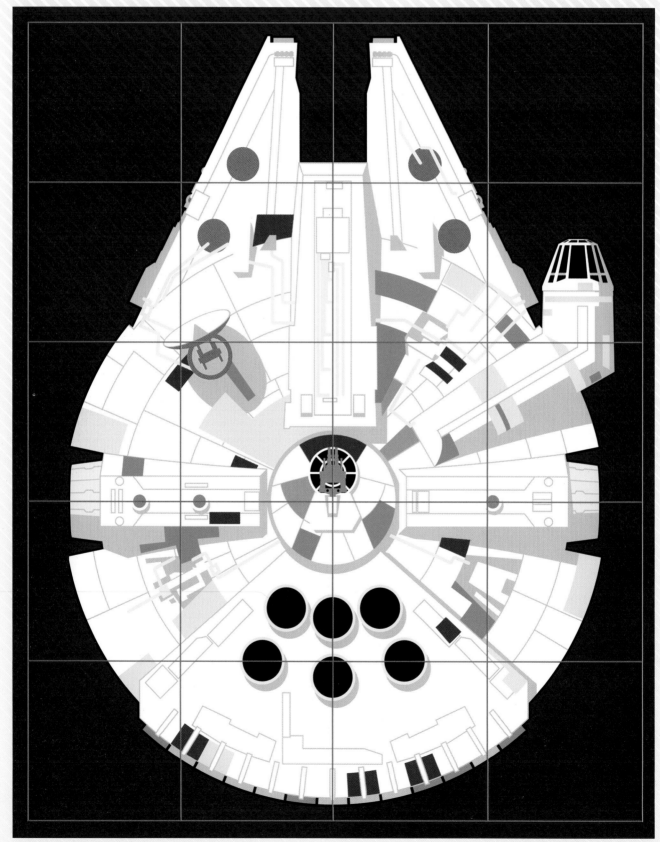

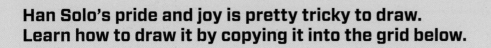

Han Solo's pride and joy is pretty tricky to draw.
Learn how to draw it by copying it into the grid below.

STAR WARS

A NEW HOPE

TM

Luke Skywalker enters a whole new world, and Han Solo gets swept up in a galactic conflict.

Darth Vader is searching for the plans to the Death Star, the Empire's powerful battle station, but Princess Leia has hidden them in R2-D2 and sent them down to the planet Tatooine. Luke Skywalker finds R2-D2 and his friend C-3PO and takes them to Ben Kenobi, who reveals that he was once Obi-Wan Kenobi, a powerful Jedi. The group set off to deliver the plans to the Rebel Alliance, paying smuggler Han Solo to take them to Alderaan in the *Millennium Falcon*. When they get to Alderaan, they find it has been destroyed by the Death Star.

Han, Obi-Wan and Luke sneak
aboard the Death Star to rescue
Leia, and as they escape, Obi-
Wan is struck down by his former
student, Darth Vader. The Rebel
Alliance now have the Death Star
plans and launch a last ditch
attempt to destroy it, sending
every ship they have to attack.
Luke Skywalker's X-wing is in
trouble and about to be shot down
by Vader when Han Solo returns
to save him. Luke reaches out
with the Force and fires the proton
torpedo that destroys the Death
Star. Luke and Han get medals for
their heroism, but even though the
Death Star is destroyed, the war is
far from over ...

THE DEATH STAR PLANS

Brave Jyn Erso led a team onto the planet Scarif and took the Death Star plans from the Imperial base – though Jyn and her team died in the attempt, she was able to transmit the plans to the rebel fleet at the last minute. The plans were taken by Leia Organa, who hid them in R2-D2, where they were later found by Luke Skywalker.

FIND LEIA!

Princess Leia Organa is being held in one of the detention cells on the Death Star, but which one is it? Help Luke and Han – disguised as stormtroopers – find their way through the Death Star to rescue Leia!

START

ANSWER ON PAGE 69 **31**

STAR WARS
THE EMPIRE STRIKES BACK

The Empire gets the upper hand while Luke learns about his father ...

Three years after the destruction of the Death Star, the Rebel Alliance, led by Princess Leia, is on the run and hiding out on the ice planet of Hoth. The Empire finally tracks the rebels down and opens fire on them as they struggle to get away. Han, Chewie, Leia and C-3PO escape on the *Millennium Falcon*, while Luke and R2-D2 travel to the Dagobah system to find Jedi Master Yoda.

Luke finds Yoda, but he is a small green alien and not what Luke was expecting. At first Yoda doesn't want to teach Luke, but Obi-Wan's Force ghost convinces him that Luke can learn how to be a Jedi. Luke promises not to quit – Yoda's training is very tough and he starts to learn more about how to use the Force.

Meanwhile, Han and Leia are still stuck on the *Falcon* because the hyperdrive won't start. They narrowly avoid the Imperial fleet by hiding in an asteroid field. Darth Vader wants to find the *Falcon* and sends bounty hunters out to look for it. Han takes the Falcon to Cloud City on Bespin, which is run by his old friend Lando Calrissian. Unfortunately bounty hunter Boba Fett has already tracked them there and he forces Lando to give Han, Leia, Chewie and C-3PO to Vader.

Luke senses that his friends are in trouble and he rushes to Cloud City, even though his training is incomplete. Vader freezes Han Solo in carbonite so that Boba Fett can give him to crime boss Jabba the Hutt. Luke confronts Darth Vader and discovers that Vader is really his father. In the duel Luke's hand is cut off, and he barely escapes with his life. Han is delivered to Jabba the Hutt – how will his friends save him?

BOUNTY HUNTERS

Darth Vader brings together the toughest mercenaries
he can find! Bounty hunters include battle-armoured
Boba Fett, assassin droid IG-88, lizard-like Bossk, battle
damaged Dengar, protocol droid 4-LOM and insectoid
Zuckuss. It was Boba Fett who earned the bounty by
delivering Han Solo to Jabba the Hutt.

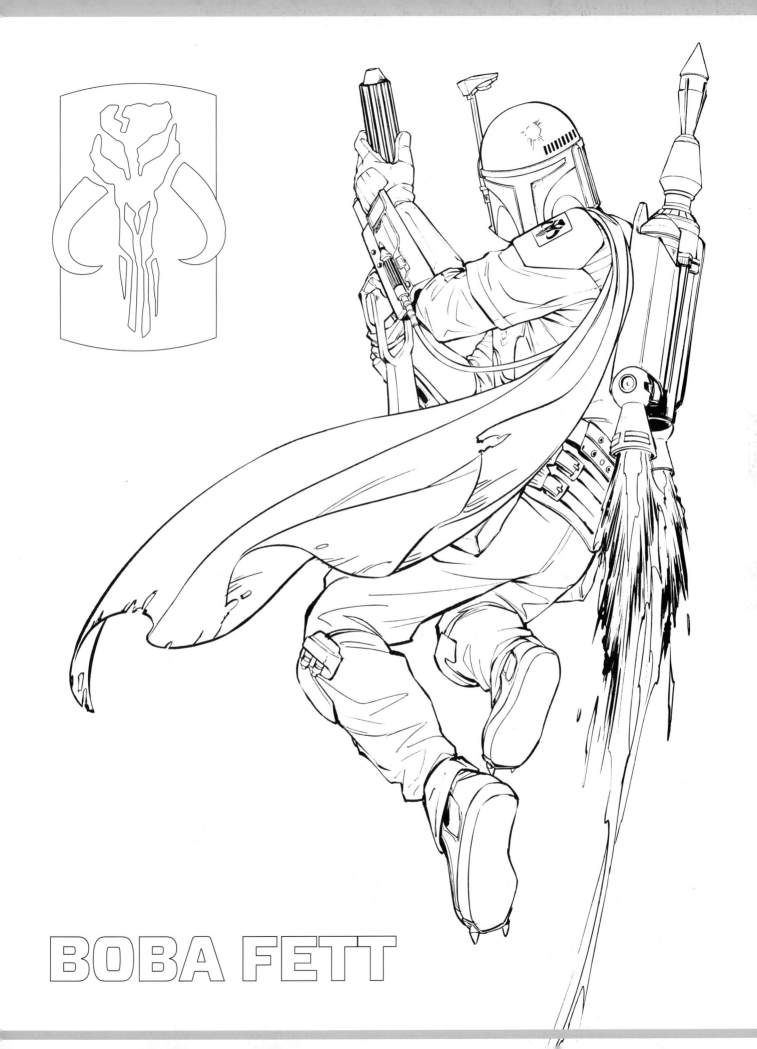

BOBA FETT

STAR WARS

RETURN OF THE JEDI

The Rebel Alliance launch a final attack against the Empire, while Luke confronts Darth Vader.

Luke Skywalker returns to Tatooine to rescue Han Solo from crime lord Jabba the Hutt. Meanwhile, Princess Leia disguises herself as a bounty hunter to unfreeze Han, but is captured by Jabba. Leia, Luke and Han are taken to the Sarlacc, a giant underground monster, but they manage to escape, killing Jabba and Boba Fett in the process. Luke returns to Dagobah to finish his training, but Yoda dies after

telling him that he has a sister, who Luke discovers is Leia.

The Empire has nearly finished building an even bigger Death Star. The Rebel Alliance plan their strategy to destroy the battle station before it becomes fully operational. Han Solo leads a strike team to the suface of the Endor moon in order to destroy the shield generator protecting the Death Star.

Once in the forests of Endor, the team come under attack from stormtrooper scouts and realise that they are outnumbered. Thankfully, Leia befriends the native Ewoks, and convinces them to help in the battle against their Imperial occupiers. The tribe fight valiantly alongside Han, Leia and the other rebels until they are able to enter the bunker and disable the shield generator.

Luke goes to Emperor Palpatine and Darth Vader on the Death Star. The Emperor tells Luke that his friends will soon be dead and tries to turn Luke to the dark side. Luke refuses to turn, but isn't strong enough to stand up against the Emperor's Force lightning. Darth Vader redeems himself by saving his son Luke and killing the Emperor.

With the shield generator now deactivated, Lando and Nien Nunb fire the winning shot at the reactor core and destroy the Death Star.

The Empire is finally defeated!

AFTER THE EMPIRE

Everything changed after the Battle of Endor. The Empire had been crushed, so the Rebel Alliance became the New Republic and tried to bring peace to the galaxy. Meanwhile, the shattered remains of the Empire slowly regained strength and became the First Order.

Leia Organa sensed that the First Order were a danger to the galaxy. She founded the Resistance, but even she didn't realise how strong the First Order had already become.

HIDDEN REBEL

Find the rebel hero who led the team to destroy the shield generator.

Clue: They only appear once in the grid.

KNOW YOUR DROIDS!

There are lots of different types of droids in the *Star Wars* galaxy – here's how to tell them apart.

SECURITY DROIDS

These deadly droids were designed to provide protection to people or objects of value. Their primary objective was to defend and even destroy perceived threats. They were used by Imperial forces to enforce the will of the Emperor. K-2SO was reprogrammed to become loyal to the Rebel Alliance, using his appearance to infiltrate Imperial outposts.

ASTROMECH DROIDS

Piloting a starfighter is a tricky job, and most humans needed a droid to help them fly the ship, calculate hyperspace jumps and perform simple repairs. Most astromechs could only talk in a series of beeps known as binary, but once connected to a starship they could print words on a screen. BB-8 and R2-D2 are both astromech droids, and can fit in X-wing fighters.

BATTLE DROIDS

During the Clone Wars the droid army was made up of many different types of battle droids. The standard battle droids were the rank and file soldiers, while the super battle droids were bigger, faster and tougher. The massive droidekas (also known as rollies) carried their own deflector shields and were tough enough to fight Jedi.

PILOT DROIDS

Some droids were used to pilot starships, starfighters and much bigger ships. Lando Calrissian's co-pilot on the *Millennium Falcon* was L3-37, a self-created pilot droid who cared very deeply about droid rights.

PIT DROIDS

Some droids were programmed for more menial tasks, and these useful robots were designed to be cheap and dependable. Pit droids were used to repair and service podracers on Tatooine. They could be folded away by tapping them on the nose when they were not needed.

PROTOCOL DROIDS

Droids like C-3PO were built to translate between people speaking different languages, and to help with different customs. When C-3PO first met Luke Skywalker, he claimed he was fluent in six million forms of communication, which had been upgraded to seven million by the time he met Finn and Poe.

IMPERIAL PROBE DROIDS

These droids could be used to search the galaxy for people and wouldn't stop until they had found what they were looking for, or they were blasted out of the sky! Han Solo shot down a probe droid on Hoth when the Empire was searching for the Rebel Alliance.

DESIGN YOUR OWN DROID

What would your ideal droid look like? You could pick bits from other droids or choose something completely different! Draw your droid below!

ARMS

LEGS

WEAPONS

STAR WARS

THE FORCE AWAKENS

™

Rey and Finn join the fight against Kylo Ren and the First Order.

Thirty years after the Battle of Endor, the Galactic Empire has been reborn as the First Order, and is trying to destroy the New Republic. Luke Skywalker is missing, but General Leia Organa sends her best pilot, Poe Dameron, to the planet Jakku to find a map to Luke's location. Poe hides the map in his droid BB-8 before he is captured by Kylo Ren and the First Order. BB-8 meets Rey, who saves him from other scavengers. Meanwhile Finn, a stormtrooper who wants to leave the First Order, helps Poe escape, but their TIE fighter is shot down over Jakku.

Finn meets Rey and BB-8, telling them that he is a member of the Resistance. First Order TIE fighters blast Jakku, so Finn, Rey and BB-8 escape in the nearest ship, a "junk" ship that turns out to be the *Millennium Falcon*. Almost as soon as they leave Jakku, the *Falcon* is pulled in by a bigger ship's tractor beam and boarded by Han Solo and Chewbacca, anxious to get their beloved freighter back. Han's ship becomes a battleground when two underworld gangs attack him and then deadly rathtars are released. Finn, Rey, Han, Chewie and BB-8 escape on the *Millennium Falcon*, narrowly avoiding being chomped by the massive aliens.

Han takes everyone to Takodana to meet Maz Kanata at her castle. Rey finds Luke Skywalker's old lightsaber and experiences Force visions when she touches it. The First Order attack Takodana, and during the fight Rey is captured by Kylo Ren. In the nick of time Poe arrives, leading a squad of Resistance X-wings to fight off the First Order and save the day.

The First Order have a giant battle station called Starkiller Base, which they use to destroy the New Republic's capital Hosnian Prime. Kylo Ren tries to interrogate Rey on Starkiller Base, but the Force is strong with her and she resists. Han, Chewie and Finn arrive on Starkiller Base to save Rey and destroy the station, but Rey has already freed herself. To buy time Han Solo tries to talk to his son Kylo Ren, but he has gone too far to the dark side of the Force. Kylo stabs his father with a lightsaber, and Han falls to his death.

While Poe Dameron's X-wing squad blast Starkiller Base, Rey and Kylo Ren face off for a dramatic lightsaber battle! Finn tries to protect Rey and is badly hurt, but Rey uses the Force and beats Kylo Ren, as Starkiller Base disintegrates around them. Rey, Finn and Chewie escape on the *Millennium Falcon*, while a scarred Kylo Ren lives to fight another day.

Back at the Resistance base, R2-D2 finally puts the map together to find the location of Luke Skywalker. Rey takes Chewie and the *Falcon* to the ocean planet of Ahch-To, where she finds Luke ... and hands him his lightsaber.

RESISTANCE WORDSEARCH

Can you find all the hidden words in this wordsearch? The Resistance is counting on you!

S	T	A	R	K	I	L	L	E	R	B	A	S	E
D	P	K	R	S	F	Q	B	Y	E	C	L	K	L
R	O	A	Y	R	U	I	Y	R	Y	H	K	Y	U
A	E	T	F	L	N	Y	N	E	S	E	T	W	K
M	D	R	L	E	O	L	U	N	R	W	S	R	E
M	A	I	O	I	E	R	G	S	A	B	K	E	S
A	M	N	R	A	K	M	E	U	T	A	K	S	K
Z	E	A	E	O	R	N	I	N	S	C	W	I	Y
K	R	A	N	R	I	C	H	I	E	C	A	S	W
A	O	G	T	G	Y	L	R	E	N	A	N	T	A
N	N	T	H	A	N	S	O	L	O	S	E	A	L
A	F	L	C	N	K	I	E	T	H	N	D	N	K
T	S	B	H	A	N	Y	O	L	A	D	A	C	E
A	E	R	S	F	I	R	S	T	O	R	D	E	R

STARKILLER BASE	HAN SOLO	FINN
KYLO REN	CHEWBACCA	MAZ KANATA
LEIA ORGANA	POE DAMERON	FIRST ORDER
REY	LUKE SKYWALKER	RESISTANCE

WANTED BY THE FIRST ORDER!

The First Order have sent down pictures of who they are trying to capture, but the holograms have become scrambled. Can you match the name to the scrambled image?

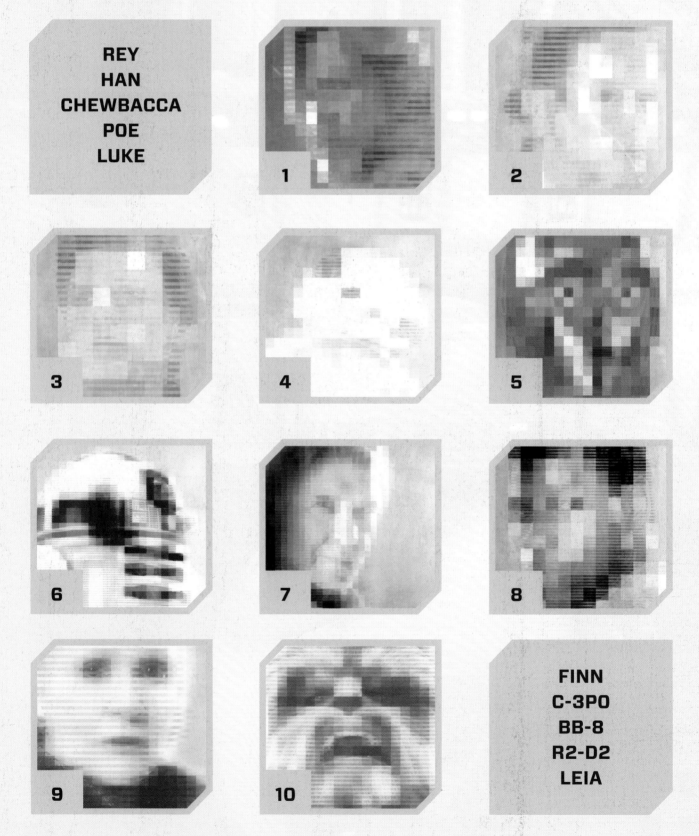

REY
HAN
CHEWBACCA
POE
LUKE

1

2

3

4

5

6

7

8

9

10

FINN
C-3PO
BB-8
R2-D2
LEIA

DROID DOUBLES

Rey and Finn want to get BB-8 back to the Resistance. Can you find seven differences between these two pictures?

STAR WARS
THE LAST JEDI

The First Order strike back against the Resistance, and Rey tries to convince Luke Skywalker to train her to be a Jedi.

The Resistance is fleeing the First Order. Poe Dameron defies orders from General Leia Organa and leads an attack against the fleet. He destroys a massive First Order dreadnought, but many Resistance ships are lost in the attack. The Resistance convoy escapes to hyperspace, but the First Order are tracking them. Kylo Ren has the opportunity to destroy his mother's ship, but instead his wingmen blow up the bridge of Leia's ship, sending her into space. Leia uses the Force to survive, but is badly hurt and can no longer lead the Resistance.

Poe doesn't like the new commander, Vice Admiral Holdo, thinking she should fight the First Order head on. Finn knows how strong and ruthless the First Order are, so he tries to escape, only to be stopped by mechanic Rose Tico. Poe sends Rose and Finn on a secret mission to find a hacker to help them disable the First Order's tracking device.

On Ahch-To, Luke tries to throw away his old lightsaber and refuses to teach Rey - after his failure to train Kylo Ren as a Jedi, he doesn't want to train anyone ever again. R2-D2 convinces Luke to train Rey, and Luke shows her the temple of the first Jedi. Rey and Kylo Ren have been communicating using the Force, and Rey thinks that there is still some good in him. Rey leaves Ahch-To to redeem Kylo, and after she leaves, Yoda visits Luke as a Force vision, instructing him to burn down the Jedi temple as Rey has learned everything she needs to learn.

Back in the Resistance fleet, Poe is angry about Vice Admiral Holdo's plan to escape from the First Order in small transports. Poe leads a mutiny against Holdo and tries to take control of the fleet.

Finn, Rose and BB-8 travel to the Canto Bight casino and are quickly arrested. They meet another hacker called DJ and bring him back to break into Snoke's starship. DJ betrays them, and everyone but BB-8 is captured by Captain Phasma.

Rey finds Kylo Ren, who immediately takes her to Supreme Leader Snoke. Rey refuses to join Snoke, and so Snoke orders Kylo to kill Rey. Kylo Ren attacks Snoke with a lightsaber and kills him, cutting him in half! Rey and Kylo Ren team up to fight Snoke's guards, and Rey thinks that maybe she can find some good in Kylo Ren. However Kylo just wants to rule the galaxy and so the two fight over Luke's lightsaber, destroying it in the battle.

Thanks to DJ, the First Order know all about the Resistance's plans, and start blasting the escaping transports. In a final act of bravery, Holdo uses her ship to ram Snoke's fleet at lightspeed, striking at the heart of the First Order and sacrificing herself. Finn, Rose and BB-8 escape and join the Resistance survivors on an old Rebel Alliance base on the planet Crait.

The First Order, with Kylo Ren as their new Supreme Leader, attack the base on Crait and the Resistance mount a last ditch defense. The First Order is about to win when Luke Skywalker steps out in front of the army! Kylo and Luke fight a lightsaber duel, until Kylo realises that this is only a Force projection of Luke and the Resistance survivors have escaped during the fight. Back on Ahch-To, an exhausted Luke becomes one with the Force and dies, while the Resistance regroup to fight again.

FIX KYLO'S HELMET

Kylo Ren has smashed up his helmet in a fit of rage? Can you help him put it back together by working out which pieces go where?

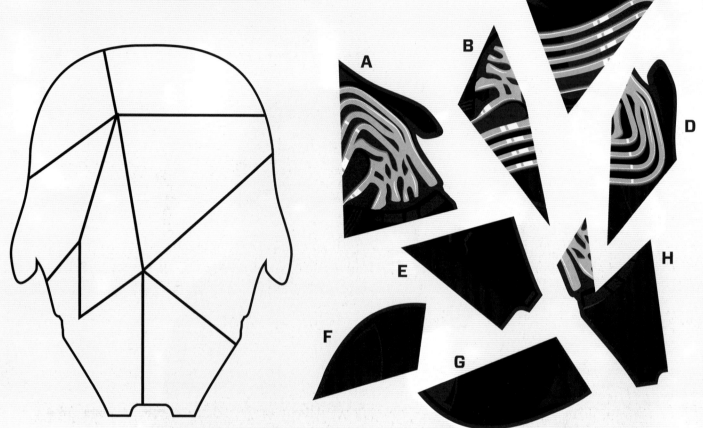

X-WING COLOURING

Poe Dameron has a new X-wing to replace the one that was blown up, but it needs a new coat of paint! Can you add a new colour to it?

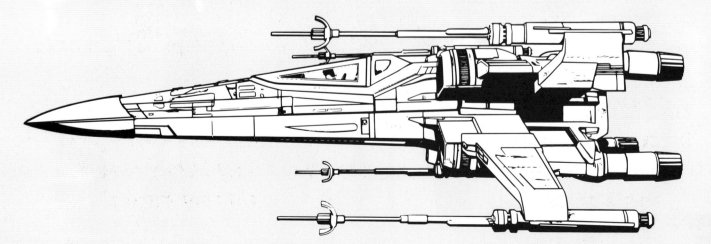

WHICH STORMTROOPER IS FINN?

Finn is spying on the First Order and has dressed up as a stormtrooper again! Use these clues to work out which one he is!

A   B   C   D

E   F   G   H

CLUE 1 - He doesn't have a black bar on his helmet

CLUE 2 - He is holding a blaster

CLUE 3 - He is only holding his weapon with one hand

REY

KYLO-REN

THE BEST ALIENS!

The galaxy is a huge place, and creatures come in lots of different shapes and sizes. Here are the coolest, deadliest and funniest aliens around!

WOOKIEES

Strong, hairy giants who are smart, sophisticated and loyal, Wookiees come from Kashyyyk and live for hundreds of years. Wookiees are normally very gentle, but they can fly into a terrible rage so don't annoy them! The most famous Wookiee is, of course, Han's co-pilot Chewbacca.

EWOKS

These furry little things don't look very dangerous, but they were incredibly important in the Battle of Endor, and helped bring down the Galactic Empire. Just don't get on the wrong side of them or they will swarm you! Wicket was a cute Ewok who made friends with Leia.

RATHTAR

Han and Chewie tried transporting these dangerous monsters, and of course they ended up escaping! They have more teeth and tentacles than should be possible, and were very nearly the end of Finn and Rey.

PORG

The island of Ahch-To is home to these cute creatures who manage to get absolutely everywhere! The porgs on Ahch-To annoyed Chewbacca at first, but he later ended up sharing the cockpit of the *Falcon* with them.

HUTTS

Hutts, as dangerous as they are disgusting, are a slug-like species who became crime lords and galactic gangsters. The planet of Tatooine was home to Jabba the Hutt, a very powerful criminal who spent a long time trying to track down Han Solo.

RANCOR

These beasts are over five metres tall and have skin so tough it can withstand blaster fire. Jabba the Hutt had a massive rancor under his throne room, and he liked to feed his prisoners to it! Jabba's rancor met his match when Luke Skywalker crushed it under a spiked gate.

MON CALIMARI

It's easy to spot Mon Calamari, just look for their squid-like heads and long fingers. These amphibious aliens come from the planet Mon Cala, and can live underwater or on land. Admiral Gial Ackbar was a great Mon Calamari leader who fought in the Clone Wars, the Galactic Civil War and the fight against the First Order.

ARDENNIANS

With their four arms, big eyes and quick wits, Ardennians are very useful in combat. They are great as pilots and also in the thick of any battle! Han Solo teamed up with Rio Durant when he joined Tobias Beckett's crew, but unfortunately Rio was hit by blaster fire during a dangerous heist to steal hyperdrive fuel.

RODIAN

Rodians are a common sight throughout the galaxy, with many bounty hunters, politicians and members of the Rebel Alliance. The most famed Rodian was the bounty hunter Greedo, who worked for Jabba the Hutt on Tatooine. He was quick to anger, but not the most skilled with a blaster, and he met his fate in the Mos Eisley cantina when he tried to challenge smuggler Han Solo.

JAWA

These tiny aliens were traders and scavengers on the planet Tatooine. Jawas travel the desert in huge vehicles called sandcrawlers, which they use to sell droids and other things that they find. Luke bought C-3PO and R2-D2 from Jawa traders.

ALIEN SPOTTING

Can you work out which aliens these are just from the close ups?

1

2

3

4

5

6

7

8

9

10

ANSWERS

17 Podrace Shortcut: B

19 Odd Clone Out

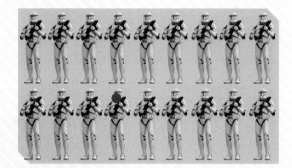

21 Sith Sudoku

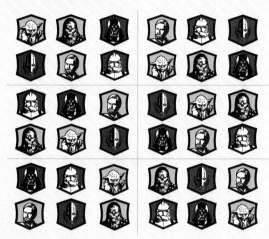

31 Maze

39 Hidden Rebel

47 Resistance Wordsearch

48 Wanted by the First Order!

1. Luke
2. Rey
3. Poe
4. BB-8
5. C3-PO
6. R2-D2
7. Han
8. Finn
9. Leia
10. Chewbacca

49 Droid Doubles

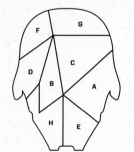

54 Fix Kylo's Helmet

55 Which Stormtrooper is Finn?: F

54 Alien Spotting

1. Jawa
2. Porg
3. Rodian
4. Rancor
5. Mon Calimari
6. Rathtar
7. Ewok
8. Wookiee
9. Ardennian
10. Hutts